Devon's Geology
an introduction

Robert Hesketh

Bossiney Books · Launceston

Introduction

Devon has some of the most dramatic, beautiful and varied geology and therefore landscape anywhere in Britain. This short book is designed for people with little or no previous geological knowledge who want to understand such features as the magnificent red sandstone cliffs in the east of the county, the fantastically contorted rock strata at Hartland, or the sculptured granite of Dartmoor. A selection of the best geological sites and directions for finding them are given, along with photographs to aid identification.

Every major geological period except the most ancient is well represented in Devon, a span of approximately 400 million years. Not surprisingly, much pioneering geological work has been done here. The area has long been a magnet for students – nowhere else can so much be studied in such a modest and pleasing compass.

It is the only British county to have given its name to a geological system known all over the world, the Devonian. Devon also has part of Britain's first natural World Heritage Site – the dramatic and fascinating 'Jurassic Coast' between Exmouth and Studland in Dorset.

With so much to seek out, you're almost spoilt for choice. Armed with an enquiring mind and a map (preferably an Ordnance Survey 1:25,000 *Explorer*), a basic understanding of geology will add an extra dimension to any walk or drive, or just a day at the beach. In case the subject really grabs you, there is a list of books and geological maps for further study on page 32.

Robert Hesketh

This reprint 2008
First published 2006 by Bossiney Books Ltd
Langore, Launceston, Cornwall PL15 8LD   www.bossineybooks.com
ISBN 978-1899383-89-4
Acknowledgements
We are grateful to *Devon Life* for permission to reproduce material based on 'Hesketh's Miscellany'. The maps are by Graham Hallowell: that on page 16 is based on one in *The Geology of Devon* by EM Durrance and DJC Laming, by kind permission of the University of Exeter Press. The photograph on page 30 is reproduced by kind permission of Kent's Cavern and that on page 8 is by Paul White. All other photographs are by the author.
Printed in Great Britain by R Booth Ltd, Penryn, Cornwall

Baggy Point seen from the coast path

1 The Devonian Period, c. 395-345 million years ago

Devon's oldest datable rocks were formed when Britain was part of a large landmass, the Old Red Sandstone Continent. Under tropical seas, sandstones and shales were deposited in both north and south Devon. In shallower waters, sea creatures thrived. Their remains formed the massive limestone beds around Plymouth and Torquay – where later erosion carved the remarkable Kent's Cavern. There are also limestone caves at Chudleigh and Buckfastleigh (pages 29 to 30).

Devonian rocks occupy two broad belts, one south of Dartmoor and one in north Devon, north of a line drawn from Croyde eastwards into Somerset. The Devonian period is most easily understood by visiting the north Devon coast – ideally by walking the coast path.

Geological maps of north Devon show an orderly succession of rock strata, starting with the oldest, the Lynton Beds, in the east. Westwards, the rocks are arranged in long thin bands running south-eastwards into Somerset: the Combe Martin, Ilfracombe, and Morte Slates, followed by the Pickwell Down Sandstones, Baggy Sandstones and Pilton Shale. To make matters simpler, the rocks are named after coastal settlements.

Above: Morte Point   Opposite: Westcombe Beach near Ringmore

One of the most accessible and interesting sites in north Devon is Baggy Point near Croyde, where two bands of ancient rock meet. From the top of the cliff on Baggy Point at SS422409, Baggy Sandstone can be seen resting on Upcott Slate. As usual, the best view is from the coast path.

Getting to Baggy Point: Use the National Trust car park in Croyde (SS433397). Follow the well-surfaced cliff path. Ridges of shale stretch out into the foaming sea. The Baggy Sandstone is revealed as you approach Baggy Point.

Further examples of north Devon formations can be seen at many places along the coast. Morte Point (SS440456, accessible via the coast path from the car park at Mortehoe) offers a dramatic view of saw-toothed Morte Slates, the death of many ships. Lee Bay (SS694495, parking near the beach) shows clearly defined shale formations. A variety of interesting formations can also be seen from the Kiln car park at Combe Martin (SS578473). To the east are Lester Slate and Sandstones, clearly exposed within the Ilfracombe Slate. To the west is limestone within Combe Martin Slate.

In south Devon, the Devonian period is less clearly defined than in north Devon. The strata were not laid in such an orderly fashion. Often, they were interbedded and distorted by tectonic forces.

This is especially true in Torbay, which has a complicated but fascinating combination of rocks from the Devonian, Permian, Triassic and Jurassic periods. A good example is at Waterside (Oyster) Cove, Goodrington. Coarse limestone and Torbay Breccias (formed from fragments of existing rock) overlie the older Devonian slates and sandstones. From Oyster Cove there are good views north to Roundham Head, a dramatic combination of Red Aeolian Sandstone with Torbay Breccias and the limestone of Armchair Rock.

Getting there: Waterside Cove is just east of Goodrington Church – roadside parking. It is reached via Oyster Bend and a railway footbridge (SX895587).

Despite the complications, a general pattern in the South Hams is shown by the shape of the coastline. Draw an imaginary line from Dartmouth in the east to Wembury in the west. The coastline southwards resembles a sandwich. A broad northerly band of rocks, Dartmouth Slates, forms the top layer of the sandwich. This layer reaches as far south as a line from Strete to Westcombe and is Devon's earliest datable formation.

Scabbacombe Beach

Southwards to the Start Boundary Fault, which stretches from Hallsands to Bolt Tail, is a narrower band, representing the 'sandwich filling' of less resistant Meadfoot Slates. They have been more severely eroded by the sea than either the Dartmouth Slates to the north or the schists in the southern tip of Devon. Being harder, schists and Dartmouth slates also have higher cliffs, proof of their better resistance to other erosive forces such as wind and rain.

One of the best places to see Dartmouth and Meadfoot Slates is where they meet at Westcombe Beach, near Ringmore (see photo on page 5). This is on the west-facing coast of the South Hams, at SX636457. (Don't confuse it with Ringmore near Shaldon.) Northward, the hard, shiny Dartmouth Slates jut out. To the south, the Meadfoot Beds have been severely cut back by the sea.

Getting to Westcombe Beach: Park at Ringmore. Walk 1.5km (1 mile) west on the coast path.

At Scabbacombe Sands (SX923517), south of Brixham, a transitional passage from Dartmouth to Meadfoot slate is exposed. Due to folding and faulting, the two slates appear together like the locked fingers of a hand.

Getting to Scabbacombe Sands: Follow the signs for Coleton Fishacre from the A379 Kingswear road and park at SX911513. Take the coast path link, 1.5km (1 mile).

The extreme southern tip of Devon is separated from the rest of the county by a major tectonic line, the Start Boundary Fault, and consists of resistant schists – the southern layer of our rocky sandwich. As schists contain no fossils, their age can only be assessed indirectly, but it is generally agreed they are ancient and are thus placed in the Devonian group. Like slate, schist is a metamorphic rock, one which has been altered by heat and/or pressure within the Earth's crust. As a result, metamorphic rock is partially or fully re-crystallised to form a new rock, often containing new minerals. Dartmoor granite is a prime example.

Between the spectacular headlands at Start Point (SX830370) and Bolt Tail (SX669398), schists form the southern rampart of Devon both geographically and geologically.

They also extend beneath the Channel, both westwards and southwards beyond Prawle Point (SX772349).

Getting there: Park at Hope Cove, Bolberry, Start Point or East Prawle. Follow the coast path.

Brent Tor near Lydford

2 The Carboniferous Period, 345-280 million years ago

Most rocks west of the River Exe and between the Devonian strata in the far north of Devon and south of Dartmoor belong to the Carboniferous Period, so called because coal strata were formed elsewhere at that time. In Devon during the Carboniferous, a thick succession of sandstones, mudstones and shales were deposited under the sea. Where the sea was shallow, vegetation built up sooty carbonaceous deposits, known locally as Culm. A broad zone across central Devon is called the Culm Measures. Underlying rocks dictate soil type to a large extent. Culm soils are heavy to work and acidic. Consequently, they have traditionally been used for grazing.

There was widespread volcanic activity during the Lower (earlier) Carboniferous Period. Brent Tor (SX472804) on the western edge of Dartmoor is a classic example of such volcanic activity, though it may date back to the Upper Devonian. At 334m (1092ft), crowned with a tiny Norman church and the remains of an Iron Age hill fort, Brent Tor is a landmark for miles around. It is composed of volcanic breccia and pillow lava, exuded beneath a former sea. Frost shattering and wind erosion have worn this conical hill into steps.

Getting to Brent Tor: 5km (3 miles) south west of Lydford. Use the small car park opposite the tor. Don't leave valuables in the car.

As well as volcanic activity, some rocks were changed by heat. Low level heat (in geological terms) turned many shales into slates in both north and south Devon. Greater heat created the schists described in chapter 1.

During the later Carboniferous and on into the following Permian, rocks were folded and faulted. This mountain-building period had dramatic effects on Devon. Mountains up to 3000m (10,000ft) high were formed – but today Devon's highest peak is High Willhays on Dartmoor, barely a mountain at just over 621m (2039ft).

Folding and faulting from the Carboniferous is still highly visible at many places along the coasts of north and south Devon, as well as some inland locations. The Crackington Formation offers a classic example. These rocks, sheets of interbedded sandstone and shale, fantastically contorted, form the bulk of the cliffs southwards from Hartland Point (SS228277) to the Cornish border and on to Crackington Haven. This stretch of the coast contains some of the highest and steepest cliffs in Devon, as everyone who has walked the coast path can testify. However, superb examples of the Crackington Formation can be seen quite easily at Hartland Point and especially from Hartland Quay (photo below, SX472804).

Getting there: Use the car park at Hartland Quay, 4km (2.5 miles) west of Hartland village. For Hartland Point, use the car park near Blagdon Farm and follow the coast path west for 500m (550 yards).

3 The Granite Intrusion, c. 280 million years ago

More dramatically still, an enormous chamber of molten rock (a batholith) formed beneath Devon and Cornwall. Later erosion exposed this batholith as the granite of Dartmoor and the related granite outcrops down the spine of Cornwall.

As it cooled to 1000°C, this molten material solidified and fractured, usually along vertical joints. It also crystallised to form hard interlocking grains of rock, clearly visible to the naked eye in Dartmoor granite. These grains are principally quartz, consisting of grey translucent grains, feldspar (white grains, sometimes stained yellow or pink), and biotite (glistening dark brown flakes).

At this stage (late Carboniferous and early Permian), the granite was covered by 2000 to 3000m (6500 to 10,000ft) of slate and sandstone – the rocks that now surround the granite tors. As these rocks eroded, the pressure on the granite beneath was reduced, allowing it to expand upwards. Horizontal joints began to form in the granite. These can also be seen today. Usually following the lie of the land, the joints are inclined on valley side tors and horizontal on hill top tors.

Joints, both horizontal and vertical, are one of the most obvious features of granite, which lacks the layering or stratification characteristic of the slates, shales and sandstones that make up a large part of Devon and are so well revealed in the Crackington Formation (page 9). The distinctive profiles of tors – as individual as their names – have

10

Hound Tor (above) and Saddle Tor (opposite)

been formed chiefly by splitting and erosion along planes of weakness opened up by the joints. As the granite separates along these planes, it is opened further to chemical and physical erosion. Dartmoor's tors and hillsides are strewn with clitter – blocks of eroded granite.

An alternation of frost and thaw is one of the most powerful erosive forces creating clitter – indeed, Dartmoor quarrymen have long used the expansive properties of ice to great effect in splitting granite. A visit to Dartmoor in winter proves that such erosion, which dramatically affected Dartmoor during the Ice Age (chapter 7), continues. This is also true of the all too common moorland wind and rain that batter the exposed tors and – since rainwater is slightly acidic – carve curious cup-shaped depressions in the rock.

Dartmoor has a much greater area of granite than anywhere else in the West Country – 625 square kilometres (241 square miles). Haytor Rocks (SX756772), Saddle Tor (SX751763) and Hound Tor (SX744790) provide ideal examples of the geological processes.

Getting there: Haytor Rocks and Saddle Tor are on the B3387 Bovey Tracey to Widecombe Road. Continue 1km (1100 yards) from Saddle Tor to Harefoot Cross and turn right for Hound Tor (2km or 1¹/₄ miles). Use the signed car parks.

11

*Above: Blackingstone Rock, 3 km east of Moretonhampstead, is a
dramatic example of vertical and horizontal erosion*

Opposite: East Devon heath at Woodbury Common

Lesser known tors, however, are better for studying geology in peace.
Hollow Tor (SX 572746) offers a good example of vertical and hori-
zontal jointing, as does Blackingstone Rock (SX 787856) – one of
Dartmoor's best dome-shaped tors.

*Getting there: Hollow Tor is 2 km (1¹/₄ miles) north-west of Princetown.
Use the car park on the B3357 and walk 500 m (550 yards) south-east.
For Blackingstone, drive 3 km (2 miles) east of Moretonhampstead on
the B3212 and bear right at Cossick Cross (car park 0.5 km, 600 yards).*

Minerals were formed where fluids escaped along fractures in the
superheated granite as it cooled. Some of these minerals, characteris-
tically found in veins or washed into moorland streams as alluvium,
contained valuable metal ores, including copper, tin, zinc, lead and
silver. Extracting these minerals, first by streaming, later by surface
mining, and finally by deep shaft mining, had a profound effect on
Dartmoor. Abundant evidence of these industries can be found along
the banks of streams and at the many spoil heaps and runnels (open
cast workings) on the moor.

4 The Permian Period, c. 280-200 million years ago

After the folding, faulting and mountain building of the Carboniferous, Devon entered a long hot, arid period between 280 and 210 million years ago. The climate was like that of the Sahara Desert today. Devon's characteristic New Red Sandstones belong to this period and owe their colour to a thin coating of iron oxide (haematite) – a redness characteristic of hot, dry deserts as in the Sahara, the southern Rockies/Mexico and Australia.

At the same time, rivers laid down sands and gravels. Seasonal flash floods swept large quantities of sediment into the valleys and the plains fringing the deserts. Both the thick beds of red mudstone in east Devon around Sidmouth and Seaton and the Budleigh Salterton Pebble Beds that underlie the East Devon heaths are classic examples of such deposition.

To a large extent, geology determines soil type and thus land use. This certainly applies to the Pebble Beds, which are characterised by poor, dry soil, pine woods, heather, brambles and rough grass. They make the East Devon heaths quite distinct from the rich farmlands below, which support a ring of villages: West Down, East Budleigh, Bicton, Woodbury, Colaton Raleigh and Aylesbeare all lie on the well watered marls. These marls are based on the New Red Sandstone formations and lie below the spring line.

Another place to contrast the Pebble Beds and New Red Sandstone is the Otter Estuary at Budleigh Salterton. The cliffs in front of you are Otter Sandstone; the pebbles beneath your feet are part of the Pebble Beds which the sandstones overlie. The beds, up to 160 m (528 ft) thick, extend over an area of 120 square kilometres (46 square miles) up the Otter Valley. Beneath them lies Devon's largest aquifer – 200 billion litres (50 billion gallons) of water.

Getting there: From Budleigh Salterton's Lime Kiln car park (SY073820) walk east along the beach.

Whilst some of Devon's New Red Sandstones were created from wind-blown sand (Aeolian Sandstones), some were deposited by rivers (Fluvial Sandstones) and the Otter Sandstones were formed by both processes. Some of these sandstone deposits are 3000 m (10,000 ft) thick and show similar characteristics to other red bed formations around the world.

   The railway cuttings near Dawlish offer superb examples of Aeolian New Red Sandstone. The largest cross bed section is 20 m (66 ft) thick at SX962761, in the cliff behind Coryton's Cove. This gives a vivid idea of the huge sand dunes which created these formations when Devon resembled the Sahara.

Getting there: Park at Dawlish town centre. Follow the coast path south 600 m (650 yards) from Dawlish sea front.

Fluvial New Red Sandstone near Littleham, between Exmouth and Budleigh Salterton

Aeolian New Red Sandstone at Dawlish

The long section of cliffs stretching from Torbay to beyond Sidmouth is a striking red. This gives many visitors the impression that Devon is a red county, although less than a quarter of the county's land area is underlain by New Red Sandstone. The prominent headlands east of Exmouth are an excellent example of fluvial sandstones. They were deposited in a flood plain complex of mudstones and minor sandstones, the Exmouth Formation.

Getting there: Park in Budleigh Salterton's Lime Kiln car park (SY073820), or in Exmouth, and follow the coast path. There is a good view from the sea front in Budleigh and better from West Down, SY044808, 4km (2¹/2 miles) west on the coast path.

15

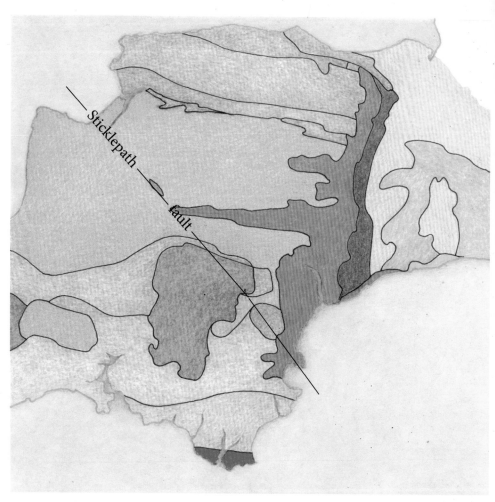

Lower Devonian schists

Devonian: slates, sandstones, limestones and volcanics

Carboniferous: sandstones, slates, cherts, limestones

Granite

Permian: sandstones (New Red), breccias

Triassic: Budleigh Salterton Pebble Beds

Triassic: Mudstones

Cretaceous: Greensand and clay

Cretaceous: chalk

Quaternary: Bovey sands and clays

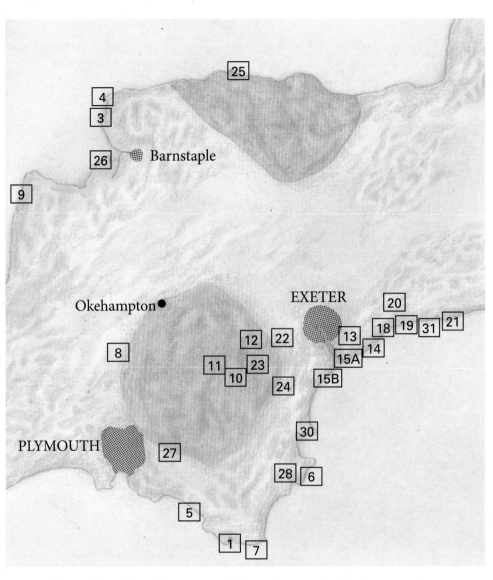

The numbers show the page on which a photograph of a site appears, and its approximate location on the map.

All the sites detailed in this book are open to the public, mainly with open access, though any restrictions or charges are described. Please follow the Fieldwork Code on page 32 for your own safety and to preserve geological sites for the future.

Isolated stacks towering out of the sea at Ladram Bay

Another fine example of this kind of erosion is the Parson and Clerk mid-way between Teignmouth and Dawlish at SX 961746

The east-facing coast between Budleigh Salterton and Sidmouth is sheltered from the prevailing south-westerly winds and so, to some extent, from erosion by the sea. Thus erosion is slower than around Exmouth or east of Sidmouth. Isolated pinnacles of partly eroded sandstone survive as sea stacks at Ladram Bay.

Getting there: From Otterton take the lane for Ladram Bay. Go through the caravan park (SY097852).

Higher Dunscombe Cliff 2km east of Sidmouth at SY152877. Red Sandstone capped with Greensand, clay and flints

5 Jurassic and Cretaceous Periods, 200-65 million years ago

At the end of the Triassic Period, sea levels rose. It is likely that central and northern parts of Devon formed an island, whilst southern and eastern parts of the county were under the sea. The Jurassic Period in Devon is represented by the thin limestones and shales deposited in shallow tropical seas and found in the extreme south-east of Devon, east of the Axe Valley and on into Dorset.

The Upper Greensands of East Devon, found on the cliff peaks and on the tops of the Blackdowns and Haldon Hills, were deposited on an ancient shoreline.

A splendid example is Peak Hill near Sidmouth (SY105859). The base of Peak Hill, which rises 157m (518ft) above the sea and dominates the view west of the town, is New Red Sandstone. However, its cap, 18m (60ft) thick, is Upper Greensand and clay with flints. Walking or driving up Peak Hill, the change in underlying rock is marked by a change in gradient. Although the gradient over the sandstone is steep it becomes much steeper towards the top of the hill.

This effect is lessened on the road by a change of angle, though no such concession is made to walkers on the coast path.

The Sid Valley

Driving up the Sid Valley from Sidmouth on the A375, a similar pattern of gradients can be seen. On the valley sides, these gradients average a gentle 1 in 10 on the marls that overlie the New Red Sandstone. At the ridge tops the gradient rises to 1 in 3 on the Greensand and clay with flints.

A spring line also divides the two rock bands. Rainwater passes through the porous Greensand, but gushes out as springs on meeting the impermeable marls. Below the spring line, towards the floor of the Sid Valley, the marly soils are rich and well watered. People have established farms with good grazing and villages there over the centuries. Above the spring line, the soils are poorer and much of the ridge tops is today capped with trees.

Sea levels rose higher during the next period, the Cretaceous. A large part of the county was submerged, although Dartmoor may have remained an island. Calcium carbonate from the bodies of microscopic plankton was deposited to form the chalks of the east Devon coast. These include some of Devon's most spectacular rock formations, such as Beer Head.

Getting there: Beer Head (right) can be seen from Beer or Seaton. Park at Beer and follow the cliff path south to SY226878

The most westerly chalk cliffs in England are found eastwards from Hooken Undercliffs to Beer Harbour and Seaton. Chalk is a pure white variety of limestone, but a closer examination of Beer Head reveals distinct layers of flint banding. The whiteness of Beer Head is a powerful contrast to the New Red Sandstone cliffs to the west.

Beer Stone is a locally developed hard chalk. Best seen at Beer Quarry Caves, it is found in a 5m (16ft) thick band underground, where it has been quarried since Roman times. This excellent building stone hardens and darkens with exposure to air. It was used extensively in Exeter Cathedral, Exeter Guildhall and several east Devon churches.

Getting there: The Beer Quarry Caves are open from Easter to September at SY208881, 2km (1¹/₄ miles) west of Beer. Telephone 01297 680282 for details and charges.

Tower Wood Quarry

6 The Tertiary Period, 65-1.5 million years ago

The Jurassic/Cretaceous Periods ended dramatically around 65 million years ago with the mass extinction of all dinosaurs and three quarters of other species. This may have been caused by a traumatic collision with an asteroid.

As the curtain-raiser for the later Alpine mountain building period, the land rose out of the Cretaceous sea. In rising, it folded and faulted. Beyond the north Devon coast, Lundy granite intruded. Much of the chalk in east Devon was eroded away, leaving behind large expanses of flint both in east Devon and on the Haldon Hills. It is often exposed by ploughing on the lower slopes.

These flint deposits, although far less dramatic than the sea cliffs and Dartmoor tors discussed earlier, are nevertheless of interest. Tower Wood Quarry (SX877857) on the Haldon Ridge near Dunchideock shows a 6m (20ft) exposure of fist-sized flints formed from dissolved chalk in a clay matrix. Nearby Buller's Hill Quarry (SX882847) offers a similar exposure.

Getting to Tower Wood Quarry: Take the B3212 Teign Valley Road and head up the Haldon Ridge via Trusham to Lawrence Castle. Turn right and leave your car in the parking area.

Lustleigh Cleave

Whilst these particular disused quarries can be visited with due care, many disused quarries and all working quarries are closed to the public on safety grounds.

The Sticklepath Fault, crossing the whole county from Torbay to Bideford Bay, is a major feature of the Tertiary. One of a series of tear or wrench faults crossing the South West Peninsula from south-east to north-west, it passes along the Torre Valley north of Torquay, through the Bovey Basin and along the eastern flank of Dartmoor to Sticklepath, where an earth tremor shook the village in 1955 – and where another tremor is predicted.

The Sticklepath Fault continues through the Petrockstowe Basin to Bideford Bay and out into the Bristol Channel. Strata similar to the Bovey and Petrockstowe Basins have been found east of Lundy, under the sea in the Stanley Bank Basin.

One of the best places to see the Sticklepath Fault is in Lustleigh Cleave on the eastern edge of Dartmoor.

Getting there: Take the A382 north from Bovey Tracey or south from Moretonhampstead. Driving towards Lustleigh, the road enters the beautiful Wray Valley, a splay fault branching off the Sticklepath Fault. Park in Lustleigh (SX785813) and follow minor lanes to enter footpaths into the Cleave at Pethybridge or Hammerslake.

Subsidence caused by the Sticklepath Fault created both the Bovey Basin, between Kingsteignton and Bovey Tracey, and the smaller Petrockstowe Basin in north Devon, between Meeth and Petrockstowe, 5 km (3 miles) north of Hatherleigh. Sand and clay from weathered granite were washed into lakes and rivers and built up in these basins to form thick deposits of valuable ball clay. This has been mined for centuries.

Indeed, the Bovey Basin is Britain's main source of ball clay and is its only reserve of lignite (also known as 'brown coal'), formed from the remains of vast redwood forests. Made up of clay, silt, sand and lignite, the basin reaches a maximum depth of 1100 m (3600 ft).

As potentially hazardous industrial sites, the clay pits are strictly closed to the public. However, Knighton Heath and Bovey Heath are on the clays and are open as Devon Wildlife Trust Nature Reserves. Along with the disused clay pits at Bradley Ponds near Bovey Tracey (also open as a Nature Reserve), they show what the whole Bovey Basin looked like before industrial scale clay extraction, housing developments and modern agriculture made huge inroads into the heath, which once covered a much larger area. These reserves are noted for their heathers and gorse, as well as for birds: Dartford warblers, stonechats, tree pipits, nightjars and skylarks.

Getting there: Knighton Heath is on the B3344 between Bovey Tracey and Chudleigh Knighton at SX840774, as are Bradley Ponds, SX828777. For Bovey Heath, park by Cavalier Way, Heathfield Industrial Estate.

7 The Quaternary Period, 1.5 million years ago to today

The major geological event of the Quaternary was the succession of Ice Ages. Ice and frost shattering had a profound effect on Dartmoor's granite tors (chapter 3). It created fields of broken rock (clitter), whilst large volumes of rock were carried, often for some distance, by ice and melt water. However, unlike most of Britain, Devon lay just too far south to experience the full effects of the Ice Ages.

Great ice sheets cut northern Britain's rugged valleys, but stopped short at Bideford Bay. On the other hand, it has been argued that the Valley of Rocks (SS705496) near Lynton on the Exmoor coast provides a unique example of full glacial action in Devon. Certainly, spectacular tors and other frost-riven features mark the valley's sides, which have been further dismembered by coastal cliff recession. Now a dry valley, the Valley of Rocks once accommodated the East Lyn River, which left considerable deposits of 'head' – water and ice-borne rock. The East Lyn now flows into the sea at Lynmouth, where its erosive power, combined with the even faster flowing West Lyn, was seen to terrible effect in the 1952 flood disaster, which killed 31 people.

Getting there: The Valley of the Rocks is 1.5km (1 mile) west of Lynton on the coast road. Use the car park.

The raised beach (photo above) at Westward Ho! gives further evidence of glacial deposition in north Devon. A complex of rocks and frost-shattered debris forms a layer 6-7 m (20-23 ft) thick, principally of Culm sandstone cobbles in a sandy matrix, capped by 2-3 m (7-9 ft) of slatey material overlain in places by pieces of stony clay.

Getting there: Park in Westward Ho! Wait for low tide. Scramble down the beach between Rock Nose (SS419290) to just east of the holiday camp (SS424291) at the western end of Westward Ho! beach.

From Prawle Point (SX772349) to Start Point (SX832370), the southern tip of Devon also offers good examples of raised beaches below the schist cliffs described on page 7. Low Pleistocene (Ice Age) cliffs of sand, clay, pebbles and gravel stand at the present high water mark.

As at Westward Ho! the raised beaches are composed of head, deposited through periglacial action – processes similar to full glacial action, such as deposition through melt water from ice.

Getting there: Park at Start Point or East Prawle. Follow the coast path.

The last Ice Age consisted of eight periods of intense cold, relieved by interglacial periods when large bodies of ice melted. This melt water produced fast flowing rivers of great erosive power, similar to

rivers in the Rocky Mountains of North America today. They also cut deep valleys.

Flowing through Ivybridge, the Erme is a good example.

The river valley and gorge in the town area and north of Ivybridge have been designated a County Geological Site, because they display several features exceptionally well. Moreover, a pleasant bankside path from Stowford Mill makes the site easily accessible.

Both intrusive Dartmoor granite and the metamorphosed sediments of older Devonian and Carboniferous rocks on the margins are very well exposed. Ice Age action probably produced the outwash fan of boulders, i.e. the boulders were carried downriver by melt water, despite their great weight. The outwash fan gives this section of the Erme much of its character and is an unsurpassed example in southern England. The boulders have been used in field banks and as a traditional building material in southern parts of Ivybridge.

Getting there: Use the public car parks in Ivybridge. There is some on-road parking near Stowford Mill at SX636566.

Another deeply incised river valley is the Dart. The Lower Dart cuts through a variety of rocks on its sinuous course to the sea. There are many meanders and channels because some rocks are less resistant than others. Spurs of very hard Ashprington Volcanics (mainly basalt and tuff) at Greenway and Sharpham have restricted the river to a narrower, deeper course at those points. However, where less resistant rocks (mainly Dartmouth slates and shales) predominate, as at Broad Reach and Long Reach off Galmpton and Stoke Gabriel, the river has eroded a wider course.

Getting there: By boat from Totnes or Dartmouth (check on 01803 833206) or on foot via the Dart Valley Trail. The lane between Cornworthy and Dittisham offers very fine views and so do Greenway Gardens (National Trust SX 873547).

At the end of the last great Ice Age, many Devon river valleys were flooded by rising sea levels (caused by melting glaciers) in their lower reaches to form rias, so characteristic of the south Devon coastline. Examples include the Dart, Teign, Kingsbridge and Tamar estuaries. Geologists using seismic and borehole techniques have discovered buried river channels well beneath Devon estuaries. The buried channel of the Teign, for example, is 20.5 m (64 ft) below present levels at Teignmouth. It continues below the sea to join the buried channel of the Exe off Torbay.

28

8 The continuing story

Most of Devon's rocks are unimaginably old and the conditions under which they were formed have ranged from extreme heat to extreme cold, from mountain building to drowning under the sea. Even the Ice Ages seem very long ago in human terms. However, geology is not static, it is a continuing process. Devon gives ample proof of this.

Dawlish Warren is at the mouth of the Exe estuary, whilst Braunton Burrows and Northam Burrows lie either side of the Taw/Torridge Estuary. All three are noted for their rich plant and bird life. Whilst many Devon estuaries and rivers were drowned at the end of the last Ice Age, the channels of the Exe and Taw/Torridge partly infilled with sand (mainly wind-blown) and sediment to create the dunes we see today.

Getting there: Dawlish Warren, 2km (1 1/4 miles) north of Dawlish, car park SX981787. Northam Burrows, 5km (3 miles) north of Bideford, car park SS448311. Braunton Burrows 4km (2.5 miles) west of Braunton, car park SS446377.

Devon's limestone caves also show recent geology at work. Although the limestone itself belongs to the Devonian (395-345 million years ago), the caves have been formed much more recently by the erosive action of rainwater, which is slightly acidic due to dissolved carbon dioxide. Water works its way through joints and fissures in the rock, eventually widening them into tunnels and caverns. This process continues.

The small caves at Chudleigh Rock have beautiful and colourful calcite formations. Rainwater dissolves limestone, which then reforms inside the caves, drop by slow drop.

More spectacular calcite formations can be seen at the caves in Buckfastleigh, where a collapsed cave roof formed a natural pre-historic animal trap that yielded thousands of bones, many of them belonging to animals now extinct in Britain, such as hippopotamus, hyena and bear.

Getting there: Chudleigh Rock, B3344, SX865788. Open daily. Admission charge. Tel. 01626 852134. www.therockgardens.co.uk

Buckfastleigh Cave. Open for guided tours Wednesdays in August only. Admission charge. Tel. 01752 700293. www.pengellytrust.org

The limestone caves at Kent's Cavern, Torquay, are of especial interest. Kent's Cavern is the oldest known recognisable human dwelling in Britain. It has a wealth of prehistoric finds and spectacular geological formations. A tour of the cave reveals curtains and frozen rivers of calcite, as well as wonderful stalagmites growing from the floor and stalactites depending from the roof.

Kent's Cavern's oldest animal remains are those of a cave bear 500,000 years old. Five flint hand axes found at Kent's Cavern are 450,000 years old, when our primitive ancestors were *Homo erectus*. The more advanced Neanderthals left evidence of their lives too, principally flint implements. The earliest evidence of modern man, *Homo sapiens*, at the Cavern is a jaw bone some 31,000 years old.

Getting there: Signed in Wellswood, Torquay, SX936642. Admission charge. Open daily. Tel. 01803 294059. www.kents-cavern.co.uk

Limestone caves develop slowly, but landslips show more dramatically that geology continues to shape and change the landscape. Indeed, the east Devon coast from Branscombe to Lyme Regis is the most studied area in Britain for landslips. Much of it is protected as Sites of Special Scientific Interest and National Nature Reserves.

In recent years, small landslips have necessitated the Coast Path being moved landwards in several places. A huge landslip in 2006, just over the Dorset border at Charmouth, trapped 17 people on a beach

with an incoming tide, and one boy was stuck up to his waist in mud. It goes without saying that great care should be taken if you're walking wherever the cliffs are known to be unstable.

One of the most dramatic landslips happened one night in 1790, when ten acres of land slipped 60 m (198 ft) down and moved 200 m (660 ft) seaward to form Hooken Undercliffs. The cause was heavy rain, which made the top layer of Upper Chalk and Greensand slip over the Gault clay that separated it from the underlying Lias.

Nature has done much to clothe the damage in trees since then, creating a sheltered microclimate at Hooken Undercliffs. Walking the coast path from Branscombe Mouth to Beer Head reveals a magnificent cross section of rocks, from the red marls of the Triassic, through the whole Cretaceous succession of rocks to Upper Chalk.

Getting there: Hooken Undercliffs (SY220880) is on the lower Coast Path. Park at Branscombe Mouth (SY207883) or Beer.

Between Axmouth and Lyme Regis, the coast shows a similar succession of post-glacial landslips. The geological structure of these undercliffs essentially consists of underlying Triassic mudstones, overlain by Chalk and Greensand that have slipped seawards.

Getting there: This 11 km (7 mile) section of coast path is one of the most beautiful and unusual, but also one of the most remote. Be prepared for a long and tough walk, starting at Lyme Regis or Seaton.

31

Books, maps, CDs and websites

British Geological Survey, 01392 445271. Twenty-four detailed 1:50,000 coloured geological maps cover Devon.

Educational Register of Geological Sites in Devon, Devon County Council CD ROM, 01392 382257, www.devon.gov.uk/index/environment/natural_environment/geology/educational_register.htm This gives 80 sites with maps, descriptions and photographs.

Durrance, EM and Laming, DJC, *The Geology of Devon*, University of Exeter (1982). The major work for the serious student. Not light reading.

Kearey, P, *The New Penguin Dictionary of Geology* (1996). Useful for a subject that has many special terms.

Thematic Trails in Devon, 01865 820522, www.devon.gov.uk/geology Focuses on local sites.

www.geolsoc.org.uk/news   Events, publications.

www.english-nature.org.uk/special/geological/sites/ An overview of Devon's geology.

Safety and Fieldwork Code

The sites mentioned in this guide are open to the public, but some have restricted opening times. Please obtain permission before visiting any other sites that may be on private land. If visiting a quarry, protective clothing, including a safety helmet, is expected. Working quarries are off limits to the public.

Follow the Country Code. Leave gates as you find them, and don't drop any litter.

Do not go close to cliff edges; they can be dangerous and unstable. Take care not to dislodge rocks.

Check the tide times when visiting beaches to avoid being caught by incoming tides.

Wet rocks can be dangerously slippery.

Keep collecting to a minimum to preserve sites for future visitors. On some sites, for example Beer Head (page 21) and Budleigh Beach (page 14), rock collecting is forbidden.